The artists who have worked on this book are:

____

____

For my girls; Opal, Willow and Florence

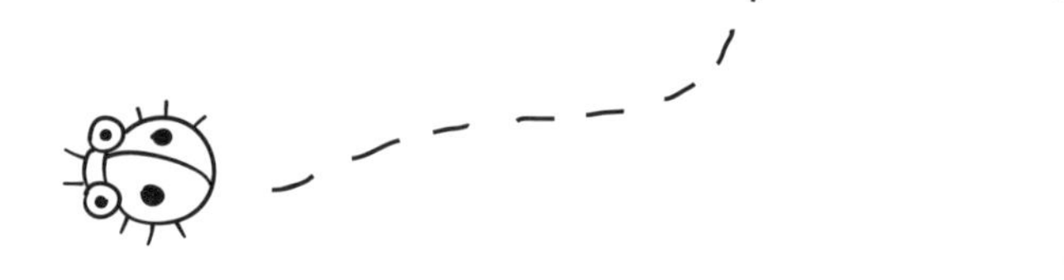

First published in 2016 by Illustrated Publishing

Reprinted in 2016 and 2019

P.O.Box 117, Te Awamutu 3840, New Zealand, Aotearoa

Printed in China by an accredited ISO 14001 & FSC certified printer

A catalogue record for this book is available from the National Library of New Zealand.

ISBN: 978-0-473-34974-5

For more about this book and other titles, visit www.illustrated.co.nz

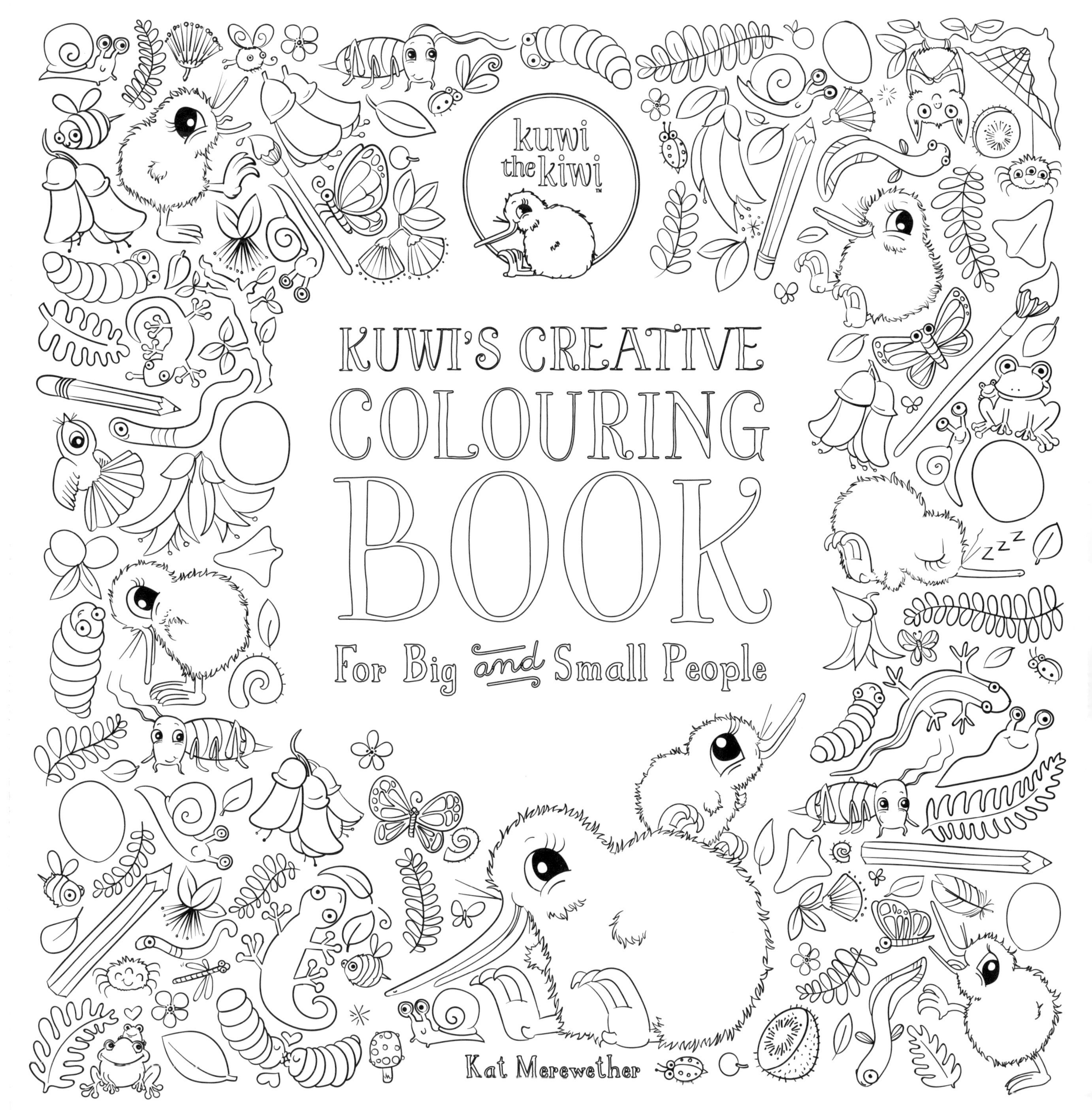
kuwi the kiwi ™
KUWI'S CREATIVE
COLOURING
BOOK
For Big and Small People
Kat Merewether

The left-hand spread has creative elements, fun facts, activities and simple colouring-in.

Perforated, easy to tear pages.

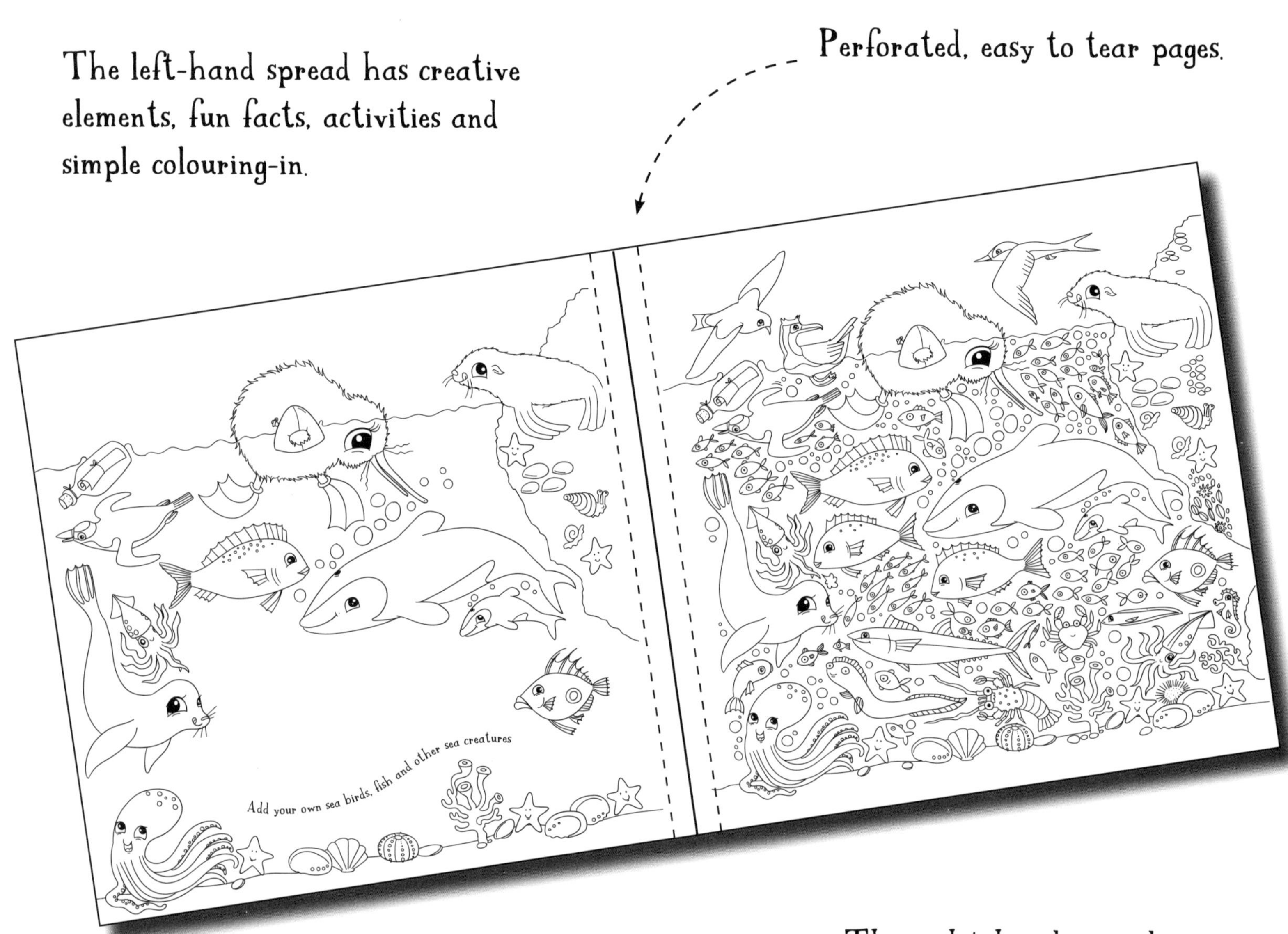

The right-hand spread is a more complex version, designed for adults or older children.

How to use this book

Work alone

This book has been designed with adult colouring and creativity in mind. The pages can be removed to create a unique piece of artwork. The simpler version on the opposite side can be left without colour so you can display the art - although, every adult is just a kid on the inside, so you may like to do this too!

Work together

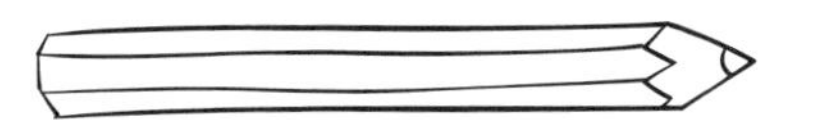

In my experience, we adults can be a little bit too 'perfectionist' to let children colour in our books. This colouring book has been designed so the child can work on the left-hand page, while the adult or older sibling can work on a similar, but more complex colouring-in page on the right-hand side. This way, younger children feel like they are 'doing what you are doing'. Happy little person, happy big person.

Nurturing creativity

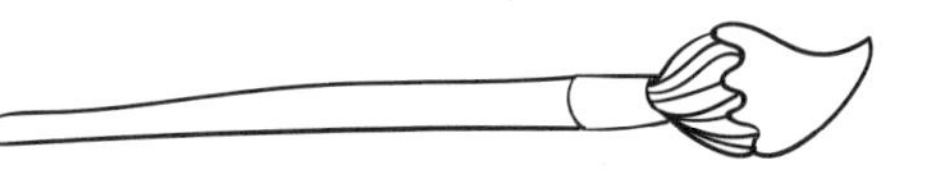

Designed for both adults and children, this book has been developed to be more than just colouring inside the lines. The artist is encouraged to add their own personal drawings and creations to the pages. It is designed to lay flat, with removable pages, for ease of use. You could make pages into a special occasion card, calendar or unique piece of wall art.

A fun way to learn facts about kiwi

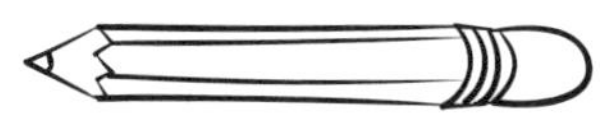

Facts about our native kiwi and other New Zealand native creatures have been scattered throughout this colouring book. Learn while you are having fun!

Add your own leaves, twigs, mushrooms and bush creatures.

Colour the frames and add your
own vintage illustrations.

DID YOU KNOW?... If kiwi are safe from predators, they can live to 50 years old!

Add your own sea birds, fish and other sea creatures.

DID YOU KNOW?... a female kiwi can lay up to **100** eggs in her lifetime.

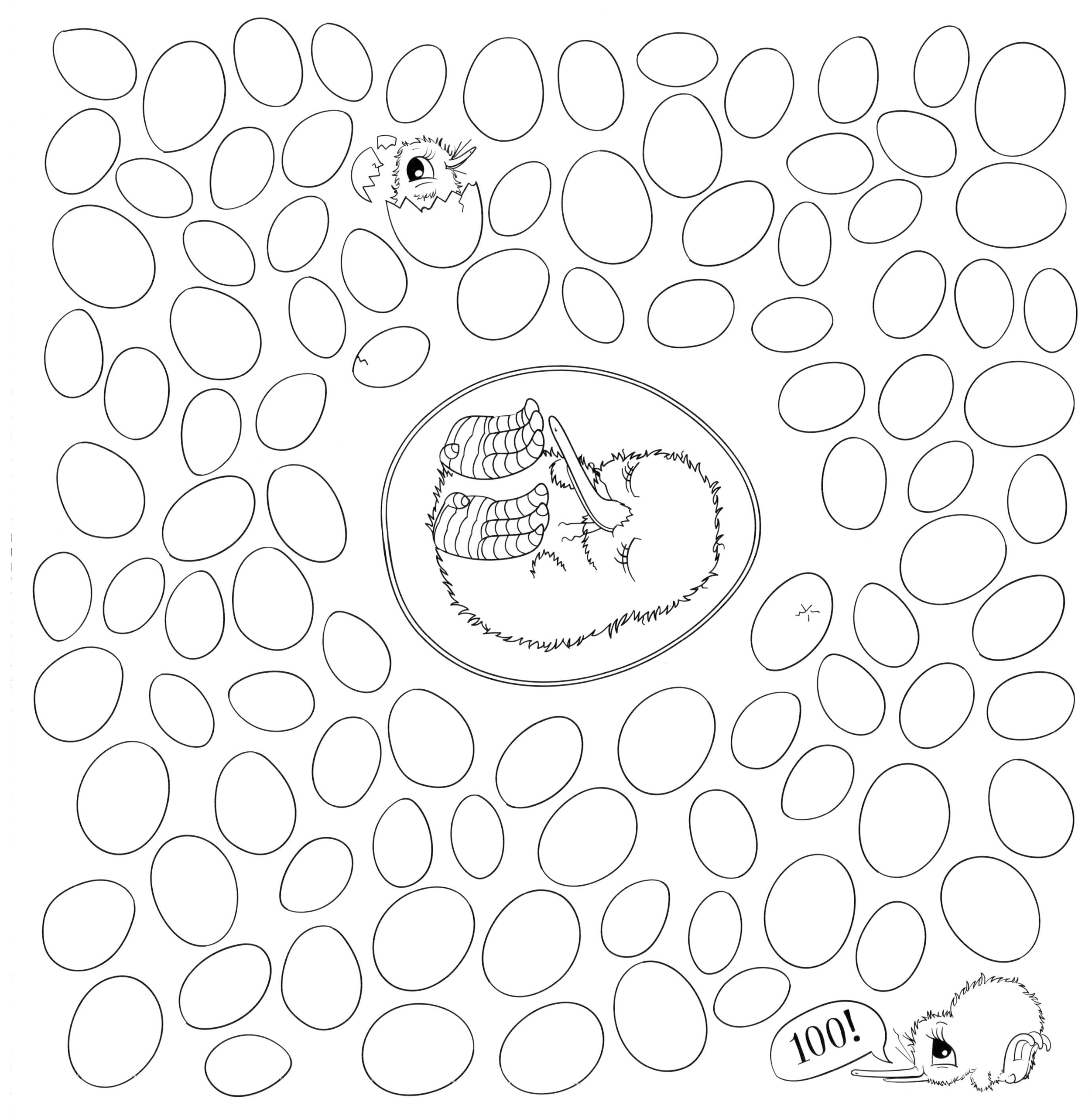
100!

DID YOU KNOW?... Kiwi chicks do not need to be taught by their Mums or Dads to find food. A kiwi chick knows instinctively to use its beak to dig in the dirt and forage for a meal.

How many tasty huhu grubs can you find in this picture?
POST
NEW ZEALAND

NEW ZEALAND
NATIVE BIRDS

NEW ZEALAND
NATIVE BIRDS

Add your own
flowers, birds and
details to the
pōhutukawa tree.

Draw some beautiful butterflies...
...and add your own details to the butterflies' wings.

DID YOU KNOW?...
Kiwi have very small wings, and cannot fly.

KIWI SEASON... The best times to hear kiwi calls in the wild are in autumn and early winter.

WINTER
SPRING
tickle
SUMMER
SPF 30+
Autumn

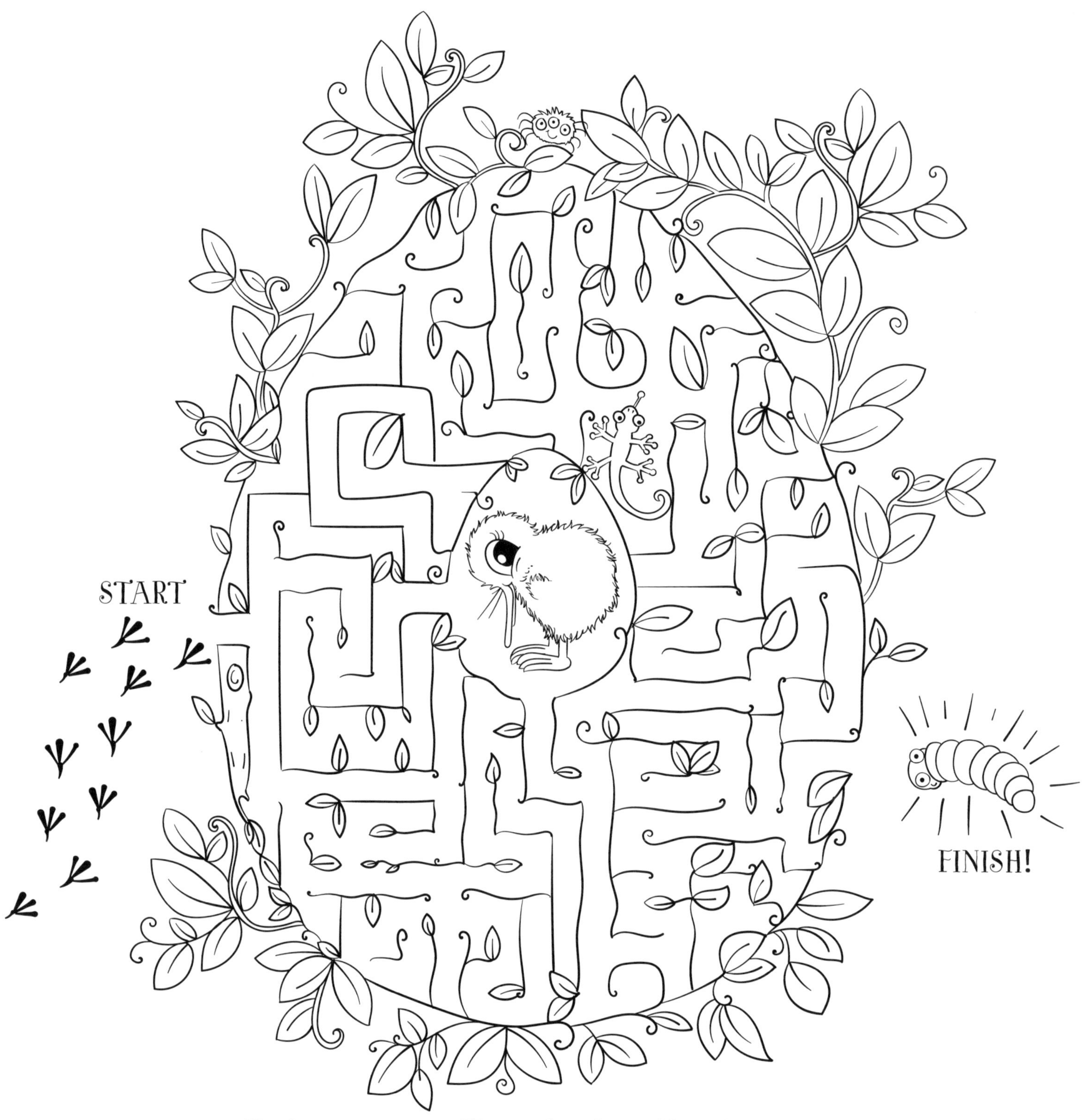

Find your way to Huwi the chick. Help him to get out of the maze, and reach the yummy huhu grub.

Add your own river creatures
and whio (blue duck) chicks.

KIWI KAI... A favourite food for kiwi is native worms. Kiwi also eat a range of insects, seeds and grubs.

They have also been known to eat fruit, freshwater crayfish, eels and even frogs.

Decorate your own kiwi egg...

MUM
Aotearoa

KIWIANA KAI

Add your favourite New Zealand kai (food) or treats.

HOKEY-PO
NZ
Tomato Sauce
fairy bread
Chocolate
L&P
feijoa
pebbles
Kiwi ♡'s Kiwi
Pavlova
WHITE BAIT
KIWI FRUIT
JET PLANES
Paua fritters
Jaffas
CHEERIOS
Choc fish

DRESS-UPS

Draw your own outfits on these four kiwi.

GS
METAL
BEAKS
Z Z
Kuwi's
First
Egg

Cuzzie bro!

DID YOU KNOW?...
Kiwi are related to the elephant bird of Madagascar, emus and cassowaries of Australia, and the extinct moa of New Zealand.

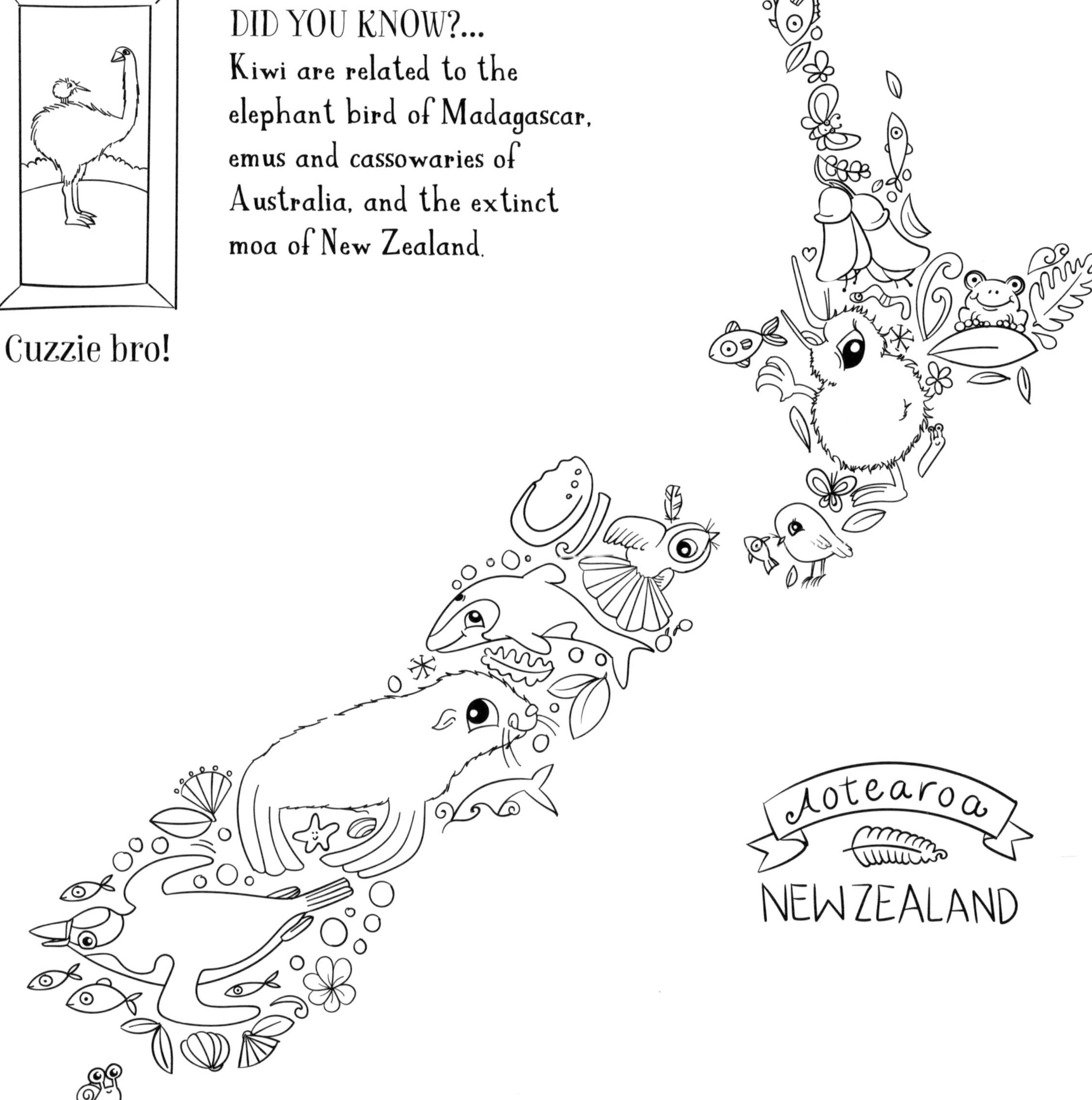

ONE (TAHI)

Perfect Pavlova

Draw your favourite toppings on the pavlova.

CREAM
CREAM

TWO (RUA)
Kowhai Trees

Add the leaves and flowers to your kowhai tree and decorate the pot.

THREE (TORU)

Beautiful Butterflies

FOUR (WHĀ)

Creepy Crawly Creatures

DID YOU KNOW?... Giant snails can live for more than 20 years!

FIVE (RIMA)

New Zealand Natives

Add your own beautiful
beach details.

SPF
30+

Illustration Glossary

Black Robin

Grey Warbler

Hoiho (Yellow-eyed Penguin)

Kākā

Kākāpō

Kea

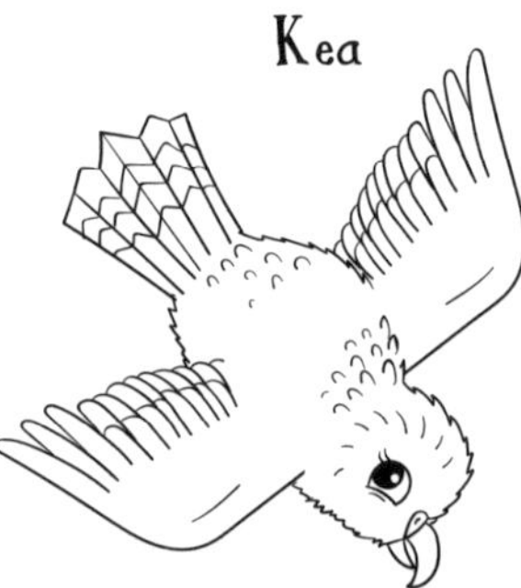

Kererū

Kingfisher

Kiwi

Kōkako

Korimako (Bellbird)

Moa (extinct)

New Zealand Storm Petrel

Owlets

Pied Shag

Pīwakawaka (Fantail)

Royal Albatross
Ruru (Morepork)
Saddleback
Takahē
Tomtit
Tūī
Whio
White-fronted Tern
NATIVE
PLANTS
& FUNGI
Kakabeak
Kawakawa
Kowhai

Stitchbird
Waxeye
Harakeke
(New Zealand Flax)
Maikaika
(Native Orchid)

Mānuka

Miro Berries

Pōhutukawa

Ponga (Silver Fern)

Ponga Koru (Fern Frond)

Toetoe

Werewere-kōkako (Blue Fungi)

REPTILES & FROGS

Archey's Frog

Native Skink

New Zealand Gecko

Tuatara

Long-tailed Bat

Short-tailed Bat

NATIVE MARINE MAMMALS
Blue Whale
Māui Dolphin
Orca
Sea Lion
Seal
NEW ZEALAND SEA CREATURES
Crab
Crayfish
John Dory
Kina
Kingfish
Octopus
Pāua
Pipi
Sea Snail

Seahorse
Snapper
Squid
Starfish
NEW ZEALAND RIVER CREATURES
Introduced Rainbow Trout
Kōura (Freshwater Crayfish)
Longfin Eel
Whitebait
NEW ZEALAND INSECTS
Cave Wētā
Common Copper Butterfly
Giant Wētā
Glowworm
Huhu Beetle
Huhu Grub

Introduced Bumblebee
Introduced Ladybird
Kahukura (Red Admiral)
Kauri Snail
Native Ant
Native Land Snail
Native Slug
New Zealand Giant Bush Dragonfly
Spider
KIWI CLASSICS
Feijoa
Hokey Pokey Icecream
HOKEY-PO
Jet Plane Lolly
Kiwifruit
Pavlova
Tomato Sauce

A little bit about Kat

Kat Merewether is an author, illustrator, and designer based in rural Te Awamutu. Fresh from the success of her books in the beautiful Kuwi the Kiwi™ series, after many requests Kat now offers a chance for creativity for adults and children alike.

Spending her childhood exploring the forest park on the slopes of Mount Pirongia, Kat's passion for conservation grew along with her talent for art and creativity. With a father involved in conservation, a love for native fauna and flora came naturally to Kat. With three young daughters of her own now, her dream of becoming a children's book author and illustrator came to fruition with her Kuwi the Kiwi™ series, Kuwi's First Egg and Kuwi's Huhu Hunt. In the first year since publication, Kat's books have featured more than 30 times on the New Zealand Bestsellers list, with Kuwi's First Egg earning a place for the top ten bestsellers of 2015.

Kat donates a portion of every book sale to Kiwis for kiwi, and through this initiative 51 kiwi chicks were supported by Kat in 2015 through the Operation Nest Egg programme. She also travels the country, teaching children about kiwi, including how to keep them safe from predation by animals, in her role as an official Kiwis for kiwi ambassador.

One of the highlights of Kat's work is to see children and adults alike enjoying her stories and illustrations. This much anticipated colouring book will undoubtedly provide many hours of enjoyment for the whole family.

OTHER KUWI THE KIWI BOOKS:

Kat with the Kiwis for kiwi team, on Motuora Island for an Operation Nest Egg kiwi release.

A little bit about kiwi

An average of 20 kiwi are killed by predators EVERY WEEK. That's a population decline of around 1,000 kiwi every year (almost 2%). At this rate, kiwi may disappear from the mainland in our lifetime. Just one hundred years ago, kiwi numbered in the millions

A single roaming dog can wipe out an entire kiwi population in a matter of days.

Approximately 20% of the kiwi population is under management. In areas under where predators are controlled, 50-60% of chicks survive. When areas are not under management 95% of kiwi die before reaching breeding age.

Only a 20% survival rate of kiwi chicks is needed for the population to increase.

How Kiwis for kiwi are saving kiwi

The work being done to save kiwi has many facets, involves many people, and is under way from the top of the North to the tip of the South Island, and on many offshore islands.

Some work is hands-on and operational—perhaps building a predator-proof fence or setting traps to kiwi predators. Other work may be research in the field to learn more about kiwi behaviour or research in the laboratory to find out more about kiwi genetics.

Some work takes precious eggs and chicks from the wild, and nurtures them in safe places until they can better protect themselves from stoats and other predators.

We also train dogs to avoid kiwi. Much of the work that is done is by communities, iwi and hapū, who together protect hundreds of thousands of hectares so that kiwi can survive and flourish.

For more info, visit www.kiwisforkiwi.org

Above: 'Kuwi' the rowi kiwi chick, named after our very own 'Kuwi the Kiwi'.

The five formally described kiwi species are:

Little spotted kiwi (A. owenii) on several offshore islands & at Karori Sanctuary in Wellington & Cape Kidnappers in Hawke's Bay

Great spotted kiwi/roroa (A. haastii) in the northern South Island

Brown kiwi (Apteryx mantelli) in the North Island

Rowi (A. rowi) at Okarito, on the West Coast of the South Island

Tokoeka (A. australis) in the South Island (Fiordland, the Haast Range & on Stewart & Kapiti Islands).